Secret-Code Math

**Kids Solve Math Problems to Crack Secret Codes
& Reinforce Essential Math Skills!**

BY BOB HUGEL

SCHOLASTIC
PROFESSIONAL BOOKS

NEW YORK • TORONTO • LONDON • AUCKLAND • SYDNEY
MEXICO CITY • NEW DELHI • HONG KONG

Front cover and interior design by Kathy Massaro
Cover and interior art by Jared Lee
ISBN: 0-590-64459-9

Contents

Introduction

Welcome to *Secret-Code Math*, a fun book of math problems designed to help students in grades 3–5 learn different math skills. Many students find math to be a difficult subject to learn. Well, it's no wonder! With all the different ways math is presented (numbers, graphs, fractions, symbols, word problems, and so on), learning math is often like absorbing a whole new language. The key to reaching students lies in giving them something they're familiar with and building from there. That's why each page of *Secret-Code Math* contains a unfinished riddle. We hope to spark your students' interest in the language and humor of the riddles in order to teach them math skills they will use for the rest of their lives. By making math interesting, we hope to open a door and let students in on a great "secret"— that math is not only important but it's also fun!

To solve the riddles, students answer the problems on the page and then use the decoder to find the letter that corresponds with that answer. Next, all they have to do is fill in the spaces at the bottom of the page to reveal the answer.

The problems cover a variety of math skills including computation, fractions, money, patterns, geometry and graphing. This wide range of skills will demonstrate to your students the fact that math is everywhere in their lives. We hope your students enjoy *Secret-Code Math* and benefit from the skills presented in this book. Good luck cracking each code!

Riddle 1

Where do cows go for entertainment?

What to Do

Find the corresponding numerals below. Then use the Decoder to solve the riddle by filling in the spaces at the bottom of the page.

1. nine _____

2. twenty-two _____

3. seventeen _____

4. forty-five _____

5. sixty-seven _____

6. one hundred eight _____

7. eighty-six _____

8. one hundred fifty-three _____

9. three hundred seventy _____

10. five hundred thirty-four _____

Decoder

23	....	X
17	....	O
153	....	E
21	....	A
370	....	O
108	....	S
76	....	D
9	....	V
15	....	F
67	....	T
22	....	E
435	....	P
86	....	H
88	....	R
45	....	I
534	....	M
118	....	W
543	....	N
307	....	G

TO __ __ __ " __ __ __ " __ __ __ __
   5 7 2   10 3 9   1 4 8 6

5

What did the helmet say to the football player?

What to Do

Find the corresponding numerals below.
Then use the Decoder to solve the riddle
by filling in the spaces at the bottom of the page.

1 nine hundred twelve _____

2 one thousand seventy one _____

3 four thousand eight hundred four _____

4 seven thousand one hundred thirty _____

5 thirteen thousand six hundred fifty _____

6 forty thousand and two _____

7 seventy thousand
eight hundred seventy five _____

8 five hundred thousand _____

9 two hundred sixty thousand
nine hundred twenty seven _____

10 one million eight hundred
seventeen thousand one hundred four _____

Decoder

4,002	B
500,000	M
10,071	A
7,130	G
9,120	Z
4,804	E
1,365	L
260,927	T
50,000	K
70,875	N
70,013	U
1,817,104	T
1,071	U
4,840	R
1,817,140	F
13,650	O
40,002	N
912	I
13,560	Y

"**YOU'RE P** __ __ __ __ __ __ __ __ __ __."
2 10 9 1 6 4 8 3 5 7

What happens when skiers get old?

What to Do

Answer each problem. Then use the Decoder to solve the riddle by filling in the spaces at the bottom of the page.

1 In the number 24, the digit 2 is in which place? _____

2 In the number 397, which digit is in the hundreds place? _____

3 In the number 35, the digit 5 is in which place? _____

4 In the number 609, which number is in the tens place? _____

5 In the number 12,706, which number is in the thousands place? _____

6 Which number is greater: 32 or 29? _____

7 Which number is greater: 168 or 174? _____

8 Which number is smaller: 802 or 799? _____

9 Which number is greater: 2,012 or 1,978? _____

10 In the number 76,549, which digit is in the ten thousands place? _____

Decoder

174 .... O
9 .... A
802 .... B
tens place L
2,012 .... W
168 .... S
6 .... M
3 .... D
32 .... H
thousands place E
0 .... G
1,978 .... U
799 .... O
2 .... N
hundreds place V
7 L
ones place I
29 .... K

THEY __ __ __ __ __ __ __ __ __ __.
4   7   2   8   9   5   6   3   1 10

Riddle 4 How do skunks measure length?

What to Do

Answer each problem. Then use the Decoder to solve the riddle by filling in the spaces at the bottom of the page.

1 In the number 52,370, the digit 2 is in which place? _____

2 In the number 619,246, which digit is in the hundred thousands place? _____

3 In the number 2,027,635, the digit 3 is in which place? _____

4 In the number 37,196,511, which digit is in the millions place? _____

5 In the number 402,819,335, which digit is in the ten millions place? _____

6 In the number 9,817,248,100, which place is the digit 9 in? _____

7 In the number 6,543,210,789, which place is the digit 5 in? _____

8 Which number is greater: 727,912 or 699,534? _____

9 Which number is smaller: 4,847,266 or 5,000,122? _____

10 Which number is greater: 7,446,726,012 or 7,446,732,011? _____

Decoder

7,446,726,012 .. **K**
ones .... **P**
1 .... **W**
4,847,266 .... **T**
7 .... **N**
thousands.......... **I**
699,534 .... **A**
hundreds .... **O**
7,446,732,011 .. **T**
billions .... **R**
tens.................. **S**
ten millions........ **B**
6 .... **E**
5,000,122 .... **D**
ten thousands.... **V**
0 .... **E**
hundred millions **M**
9 .... **F**
5 .... **H**
727,912 .... **E**

IN "SC __ __ __" __ __ __ __ __ __
        8 4 9   1 7 5 10 2 6 3

What sickness can't you talk about until it's cured?

What to Do

Find each sum. Then use the Decoder to solve the riddle by filling in the spaces at the bottom of the page.

1 12 + 7 = _____

2 32 + 10 = _____

3 50 + 4 = _____

4 13 + 22 = _____

5 47 + 19 = _____

6 97 + 68 = _____

7 204 + 41 = _____

8 37 + 331 = _____

9 670 + 98 = _____

10 857 + 466 = _____

Decoder

66 I
57 .... W
42 I
216 .... M
19 .... Y
97 C
768 .... G
35 .... S
46 .... E
100 X
245 .... R
1,257 .... D
54 .... A
52 .... O
368 L
82 .... P
1,323 .... T
155 .... Q
165 .... N

_____ _____ _____ _____ _____ _____ _____ _____ _____ _____
8   3   7   1   6   9   5   10   2   4

What's the best thing to eat in a bathtub?

What to Do

Find each sum. Then use the Decoder to solve the riddle by filling in the spaces at the bottom of the page.

1 $1,004 + 800$ = _____

2 $512 + 177$ = _____

3 $364 + 699$ = _____

4 $1,245 + 888$ = _____

5 $1,876 + 1,613$ = _____

6 $2,010 + 6,224$ = _____

7 $5,470 + 2,068$ = _____

8 $4,526 + 3,766$ = _____

9 $1,017 + 4,412$ = _____

10 $2,588 + 7,851$ = _____

Decoder

5,429	A
10,493	F
2,133	S
14,983	R
10,439	P
712	U
3,489	K
1,840	M
1,063	E
4,523	W
689	N
2,009	B
8,292	O
3,234	I
7,538	G
1,804	C
4,708	H
6,521	L
8,234	E

___ ___ ___ ___ ___ ___ ___ ___ ___ ___
4 10 8 2 7 6   1 9 5 3

When is the ocean friendliest?

What to Do

Do each subtraction problem. Then use the Decoder to solve the riddle by filling in the spaces at the bottom of the page.

1 10 – 4 = _____

2 19 – 16 = _____

3 35 – 7 = _____

4 27 – 19 = _____

5 50 – 32 = _____

6 84 – 47 = _____

7 117 – 20 = _____

8 155 – 144 = _____

9 314 – 250 = _____

10 572 – 86 = _____

Decoder

25 .... B
64 V
29 I
37 .... T
7 .... N
18 .... E
586 C
6 .... H
97 .... E
13 .... D
11 .... W
4 .... R
3 .... A
28 .... S
32 .... O
486 .... N
112 X
8 I
14 .... M

W __ __ __   __ __   __ __ __ __ __.
 1 7 10   4 6   8 2 9 5 3

Riddle 8   What tables grow on farms?

Decoder

4,884	T
64	C
275	D
459	V
286	W
1,451	B
257	L
1,541	K
428	G
81	M
743	E
48	E
792	P
2,869	S
12	Z
300	E
2,942	Y
7,926	A
7,431	Q

What to Do

Do each subtraction problem. Then use the Decoder to solve the riddle by filling in the spaces at the bottom of the page.

1   714 – 457   =   _____

2   936 – 508   =   _____

3   1,000 – 700   =   _____

4   1,362 – 619   =   _____

5   2,000 – 549   =   _____

6   3,873 – 1,004   =   _____

7   1,446 – 987   =   _____

8   5,011 – 4,963   =   _____

9   8,600 – 3,716   =   _____

10   9,925 – 1,999   =   _____

" __ __ __ __ " __ __ __ __ __ __
  7 4 2 8   9 10 5 1 3 6

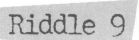

Riddle 9 What did the farmer get when he tried to reach the beehive?

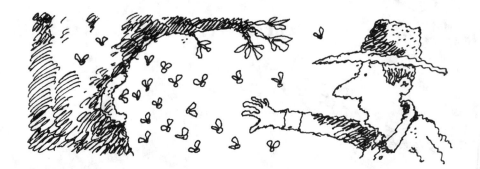

What to Do

Round each number. Then use the Decoder to solve the riddle by filling in the spaces at the bottom of the page.

1 Round 7 to the nearest ten _____

2 Round 23 to the nearest ten _____

3 Round 46 to the nearest ten _____

4 Round 92 to the nearest ten _____

5 Round 203 to the nearest hundred _____

6 Round 420 to the nearest hundred _____

7 Round 588 to the nearest hundred _____

8 Round 312 to the nearest hundred _____

9 Round 549 to the nearest hundred _____

10 Round 710 to the nearest hundred _____

Decoder

400	A
800	W
30	O
10	Y
25	E
500	I
210	J
20	L
40	C
700	U
90	S
100	T
600	G
95	F
50	N
550	V
300	Z
7	H
200	Z

A "B ___ ___ ___ ___ " ___ ___ ___ ___ ___ ___
10 5 8 1   4 9 7 3 6 2

What do cows give after an earthquake?

What to Do

Round each number. Then use the Decoder to solve the riddle by filling in the spaces at the bottom of the page.

Decoder

700	F
11,000	K
800	S
2,780	O
3,600	U
1,000	M
9,900	Y
24,400	I
73,000	S
5,000	L
24,000	P
6,000	Q
2,770	E
7,500	T
9,940	A
3,700	K
10,000	R
8,000	H
2,000	N

1 Round 789 to the nearest hundred _____

2 Round 5,112 to the nearest thousand _____

3 Round 3,660 to the nearest hundred _____

4 Round 1,499 to the nearest thousand _____

5 Round 2,771 to the nearest ten _____

6 Round 7,529 to the nearest thousand _____

7 Round 24,397 to the nearest hundred _____

8 Round 10,708 to the nearest thousand _____

9 Round 9,937 to the nearest ten _____

10 Round 73,489 to the nearest thousand _____

___ ___ ___ ___   ___ ___ ___ ___ ___ ___
 4   7   2   8   10   6   9   3   5   1

What is a tree's favorite drink?

What to Do

Find each product. Then use the Decoder to solve the riddle by filling in the spaces at the bottom of the page.

1 6 x 5 = _____

2 10 x 7 = _____

3 9 x 9 = _____

4 17 x 4 = _____

5 25 x 5 = _____

6 40 x 10 = _____

7 55 x 12 = _____

8 36 x 20 = _____

9 19 x 18 = _____

10 72 x 46 = _____

Decoder

3,321 .... D
81 L
720 .... T
4,000 .... Q
324 .... A
3,312 .... O
30 .... E
410 .... S
660 .... D
135 .... W
84 .... P
68 .... E
3,123 .... M
70 .... O
700 X
400 .... R
342 .... R
66 L
125 .... B

A CO __ __ __ __ __ __ __ __ __ __
     3 7   6 2 10 8   5 1 4 9

Riddle 12

What's the one thing you can always count on?

What to Do

Find each product. Then use the Decoder to solve the riddle by filling in the spaces at the bottom of the page.

1   100 x 40   =   _____

2   53 x 68   =   _____

3   212 x 97   =   _____

4   444 x 102   =   _____

5   832 x 366   =   _____

6   1,000 x 100   =   _____

7   2,120 x 500   =   _____

8   677 x 3,522   =   _____

9   4,000 x 231   =   _____

10   10,001 x 17   =   _____

Decoder

304,512	O
3,640	X
10,000	D
170,017	E
4,000	N
25,064	A
924,000	G
2,384,394	F
170,170	P
340,512	M
45,288	S
400	T
20,564	I
2,384,349	W
1,060,000	U
942,000	Q
3,604	R
1,600,000	Z
100,000	R

Y __ __ __   __ __ __ __ __ __ __
    5   7   2   8   3   1   9   10   6   4

Which month has 28 days?

What to Do

Find each product. Then use the Decoder to solve the riddle by filling in the spaces at the bottom of the page.

1 198 x 721 = _____

2 806 x 533 = _____

3 412 x 700 = _____

4 1,216 x 333 = _____

5 5,566 x 890 = _____

6 3,829 x 688 = _____

7 1,347 x 3,876 = _____

8 6,329 x 7,777 = _____

9 8,122 x 4,018 = _____

10 10,540 x 9,539 = _____

Decoder

142,785	B
4,953,704	U
32,634,196	O
288,400	T
440,928	W
2,634,352	E
49,220,633	H
32,643,196	N
404,928	M
282,400	S
429,598	L
100,514,060	R
49,222,636	P
5,220,972	D
100,541,060	L
142,758	F
500,000	Q
100,541,600	K
4,953,740	O

A __ __ __ __ __ __ __ __ __ __ __.
  10 2   5 1   3 8 6 4   7 9

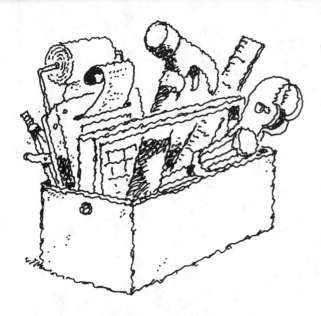

Riddle 14

What kind of tools do you use for math?

What to Do

Find each quotient. Then use the Decoder to solve the riddle by filling in the spaces at the bottom of the page.

1 $8 \div 2$ = _____

2 $10 \div 5$ = _____

3 $24 \div 4$ = _____

4 $50 \div 10$ = _____

5 $72 \div 9$ = _____

6 $32 \div 10$ = _____

7 $48 \div 7$ = _____

8 $29 \div 3$ = _____

9 $65 \div 8$ = _____

10 $92 \div 6$ = _____

Decoder

8	I
3 remainder 2	L
7	W
8 remainder 1	S
6	U
9	A
15 remainder 3	B
4	L
2 remainder 3	D
9 remainder 2	T
1	F
7 remainder 6	N
6 remainder 6	I
2	E
11	O
15 remainder 2	P
2 remainder 5	X
10	C
5	R

"M __ __ __ __" __ __ __ __ __ __
  3 1 8 5   10 6 7 2 4 9

Riddle 15 What has 18 legs and catches flies?

What to Do

Find each quotient. Then use the Decoder to solve the riddle by filling in the spaces at the bottom of the page.

1 74 ÷ 5 = _____

2 26 ÷ 9 = _____

3 41 ÷ 4 = _____

4 55 ÷ 10 = _____

5 37 ÷ 14 = _____

6 66 ÷ 22 = _____

7 84 ÷ 17 = _____

8 100 ÷ 11 = _____

9 128 ÷ 32 = _____

10 200 ÷ 25 = _____

Decoder

14 remainder 4 **M**
4 remainder 16 **L**
5 .... **P**
6 .... **O**
9 remainder 1 .. **E**
10 remainder 1 **A**
5 remainder 5 .. **T**
14 remainder 3 **K**
9 remainder 3 .. **S**
4 .... **L**
7 .... **C**
2 remainder 8 .. **S**
4 remainder 15 **N**
8 .... **E**
10 remainder 4 **D**
12 remainder 2 **U**
2 remainder 9 .. **A**
5 remainder 6 .. **R**
3 .... **B**

A BA __ __ __ __ __ __ __ __ __ __
     2 10 6 3 7 9   4 8 5 1

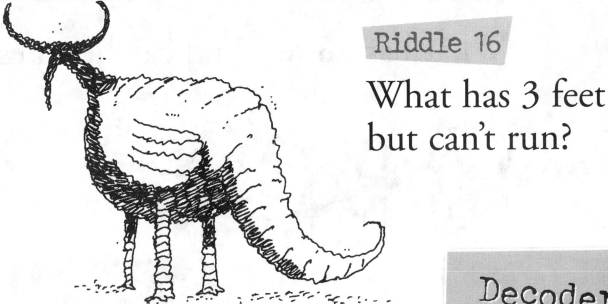

Riddle 16

What has 3 feet but can't run?

Decoder

20 remainder 10 **R**
8 .... **B**
30 remainder 40 **A**
7 remainder 9 .... **F**
11 .... **K**
6 remainder 56 .. **E**
40 remainder 30 **O**
4 .... **T**
12 .... **M**
33 remainder 12 **I**
32 remainder 12 **L**
9 remainder 7 .... **Y**
8 remainder 50 .. **N**
30 remainder 23 **D**
9 remainder 50 .. **C**
6 remainder 58 .. **S**
5 remainder 2 .... **Q**
6 .... **W**
5 .... **A**

What to Do

Find each quotient. Then use the Decoder to solve the riddle by filling in the spaces at the bottom of the page.

1 $100 \div 25$ = _____

2 $330 \div 16$ = _____

3 $407 \div 37$ = _____

4 $562 \div 84$ = _____

5 $646 \div 71$ = _____

6 $950 \div 100$ = _____

7 $1{,}000 \div 200$ = _____

8 $1{,}200 \div 36$ = _____

9 $1{,}540 \div 50$ = _____

10 $2{,}003 \div 66$ = _____

__ __ __ __ __ __ __ __ __ __
7   5 9 2 10 4 1 8 6 3

Riddle 17

What do joggers say when they leave you?

What to Do

Find the answer. Then use the Decoder to solve the riddle by filling in the spaces at the bottom of the page.

1 What fraction of the shapes are triangles? □△ ____

2 What fraction of the shapes are circles? ○○△○ ____

3 What fraction of the shapes are shaded? ____

■ ■ □ □ □ □

4 What fraction of the shapes have four sides? ____

△ △ □ □ □

5 What fraction of the shapes are circles and triangles? ____

○ □ □ △ △ □ ○ ○ □

6 What fraction of the shapes are not circles? ____

○ □ △ △ ○ ○ △ □ ○ △ △

7 What fraction of the shapes have three sides and five sides? ____

○ □ ⬠ △ ○ ⬠ △ △

8 What fraction of the shapes are hexagons? ____

⬡ ⬡ ○ ⬠ □ ⬠ △ ⬠

9 What fraction of the shapes are square and shaded? ____

□ △ ⬠ ■ ■ ○ ○ ⬠ □ ■ □

10 What fraction of the shapes are pentagons and not shaded? ____

■ ■ ⬠ △ ○ ○ ⬠ ○ □ ⬠

Decoder

1/9 .... R
6/11 .... F
4/5 .... H
5/9 .... G
2/9 .... A
1/8 .... P
2/7 .... N
7/11 .... O
3/8 .... G
7/10 L
1/2 .... T
5/11 .... W
5/8 .... U
9/10 X
3/5 .... N
1/4 .... Z
3/10 ...... T
4/11 ...... E
3/4 .... O

"SO LO __ __, __ __ __ __ __ __ __ __."
4 8   5 2 9 1 6 10 7 3

21

How does a farmer count his cows?

Decoder

5/7	U
86/102	W
2	P
7/8	S
1	O
29/40	A
12/15	D
74/237	F
19/25	L
4/7	E
2/4	C
193/237	T
3/5	U
4/5	C
84/102	I
12/13	O
21/25	J
31/40	K
7/9	R

What to Do

Find each sum. Then use the Decoder to solve
the riddle by filling in the spaces at the bottom of the page.

1 $1/2 + 1/2$ = _____

2 $1/4 + 1/4$ = _____

3 $1/5 + 3/5$ = _____

4 $3/7 + 2/7$ = _____

5 $1/9 + 4/9 + 2/9$ = _____

6 $4/13 + 3/13 + 5/13$ = _____

7 $12/25 + 7/25$ = _____

8 $9/40 + 3/40 + 17/40$ = _____

9 $39/102 + 47/102$ = _____

10 $100/237 + 14/237 +$
$71/237 + 8/237$ = _____

WITH A " __ __ __ "   __ __ __ __ __ __ __
          3 6 9   2 4 7 8 10 1 5

Riddle 19

What did one magnet say to the other magnet?

What to Do

Do each subtraction problem. Then use the Decoder to solve the riddle by filling in the spaces at the bottom of the page.

1. 2/3 – 1/3 = _____

2. 5/8 – 2/8 = _____

3. 7/11 – 4/11 = _____

4. 19/20 – 5/20 = _____

5. 27/32 – 20/32 – 6/32 = _____

6. 42/67 – 18/67 – 4/67 = _____

7. 79/83 – 11/83 – 9/83 = _____

8. 100/121 – 78/121 = _____

9. 44/156 – 29/156 – 12/156 = _____

10. 247/312 – 59/312 – 39/312 – 50/312 = _____

Decoder

1/3	T
3/165	V
1/32	A
15/20	B
21/67	F
99/312	T
61/83	K
59/83	U
4/156	L
3/8	C
11/121	W
3/11	A
22/121	T
2/32	I
4/11	U
14/20	R
3/12	N
20/67	M
3/156	E

"YO __ __ __ __ __ __ __ __ __ __."
   7   5 1 10 4 3 2 8   6 9

DICTIONARY

Riddle 20

What eight-letter word only contains one letter?

Decoder

4/5 .... N
1/7 .... Y
2/10 .... Q
4 .... P
6 C
1 L
21/29 .... M
6/12 .... N
3/12 X
6/7 .... E
56/17 .... A
5 V
18/17 .... T
5/7 I
108/187 .... E
8/3 .... S
16/6 .... O
3/2 .... B
2/35 .... E

What to Do

Find each product. Then use the Decoder to solve the riddle by filling in the blanks at the bottom of the page.

❶ 2 x 1/2   = _____

❷ 4 x 1/5   = _____

❸ 6 x 2/3   = _____

❹ 10 x 1/2   = _____

❺ 6 x 1/7   = _____

❻ 8 x 2/6   = _____

❼ 14 x 4/17   = _____

❽ 3/4 x 2/3   = _____

❾ 1/5 x 2/7   = _____

❿ 9/11 x 12/17   = _____

___ ___   ___ ___ ___ ___ ___ ___ ___ ___
 7   2   10 8   4   9   1   6   3   5

Riddle 21

Why didn't the eagle get its hair wet when it went swimming?

What to Do

Find the answer. Then use the Decoder to solve the riddle by filling in the blanks at the bottom of the page.

1 $1.00 + $4.00 = _____

2 $10.00 + $6.00 = _____

3 $9.00 – $7.00 = _____

4 $20.00 – $11.00 = _____

5 If you have $4.00 and 50 cents, how much money do you have? _____

6 If you have $10.00 and 37 cents, how much money do you have? _____

7 A dime equals 10 cents. If you have 7 dimes, how much money do you have? _____

8 A quarter equals 25 cents, If you have 3 quarters, how much money do you have? _____

9 A nickel equals 5 cents. If you have 4 nickels and 1 quarter, how much money do you have? _____

10 If you have 2 dollars, 2 quarters, 3 dimes, and 1 nickel, how much money do you have? _____

Decoder

$2.75	R
$9.00	G
$2.85	A
$16.00	D
45 cents	A
50 cents	N
$10.37	A
65 cents	F
$5.00	L
$27.00	I
70 cents	L
$4.00	T
75 cents	E
$4.50	E
60 cents	W
$5.50	M
$2.00	B

IT WAS __ __ __ __ __ __ __ __ __ __.
6   3 10 7 2   8 9 4 1 5

25

Riddle 22

How is medicine packed for astronauts?

What to Do

Find the answer. Then use the Decoder to solve the riddle by filling in the blanks at the bottom of the page.

1 A comic book costs $1.00. How much do 3 comic books cost? _____

2 A magazine costs $5.00. How much do 7 magazine costs? _____

3 A pack of gum costs 45 cents. You pay $1.00. How much change will you get back? _____

4 A soda costs 50 cents. How much do 2 sodas cost? _____

5 How much is $32.00 + $20.00? _____

6 How much is $17.50 + $40.00? _____

7 A notebook costs $2.25. How much do 4 notebooks cost? _____

8 A shirt costs $16.75. You pay for it with $20.00. How much change do you get back? _____

9 How much is $100.00 + $38.00? _____

10 How much is $220.00 + $102.00? _____

Decoder

$3.25	C
$2.00	I
$52.00	U
$222.00	W
$4.00	N
$322.00	S
$9.00	E
$12.00	R
55 cents	L
$57.50	P
$35.00	S
$55.70	D
$62.00	B
$138.00	C
65 cents	H
$3.00	E
$1.00	A

IN SPA __ __ __ __ __ __ __ __ __ __
        9 1   8 4 6 2 5 3 7 10

Riddle 23

What would you get if a pig learned karate?

What to Do

Find the answer by completing the next step in the pattern. Then use the Decoder to solve the riddle by filling in the blanks at the bottom of the page.

1 2, 4, 6, 8, ___

2 1, 3, 5, 7, ___

3 3, 7, 11, 15, ___

4 5, 10, 15, 20, ___

5 10, 20, 40, 80, ___

6 1, 5, 3, 7, 5, 9, ___

7 15, 25, 20, 30, 25, ___

8 0, 1, 3, 6, 10, ___

9 9, 18, 36, 72, ___

10 100, 200, 100, 300, 100, ___

Decoder

12 .... D
160 .... P
96 .... T
10 .... R
20 .... F
400 .... H
40 .... G
25 .... O
35 .... S
19 C
500 .... B
11 .... K
7 .... E
16 .... W
9 .... O
21 .... A
15 .... P
30 I
144 .... K

SOM __ __ __ __ __ __ __ __ __ __
   6   8 4 1 9   3 10 2 5 7

27

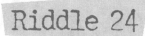
Riddle 24

How can you make the number seven even?

Decoder

5	B
1	A
97	D
215	Y
22	W
124	H
31	I
2	P
115	A
120	C
50	N
4	E
60	S
232	M
26	T
100	R
32	F
57	E
34	K

What to Do

Find the answer by completing the next step in the pattern. Then use the Decoder to solve the riddle by filling in the blanks at the bottom of the page.

❶ 10, 7, 4, ___

❷ 19, 13, 8, ___

❸ 42, 40, 36, 30, ___

❹ 56, 54, 50, 42, ___

❺ 33, 32, 34, 33, 35, ___

❻ 117, 97, 77, ___

❼ 205, 175, 150, 130, ___

❽ 344, 274, 214, 164, ___

❾ 760, 660, 540, 400, 240, ___

❿ 512, 490, 457, 413, 358, 292, ___

TA __ __ __ __ __ __ __ __ __ " __ ".
  5 2   7 3 1 10   4 8 6   9

Riddle 25

What do 36 inches and grass have in common?

What to Do

Find the answer by completing the next step in the pattern. Then use the Decoder to solve the riddle by filling in the blanks at the bottom of the page.

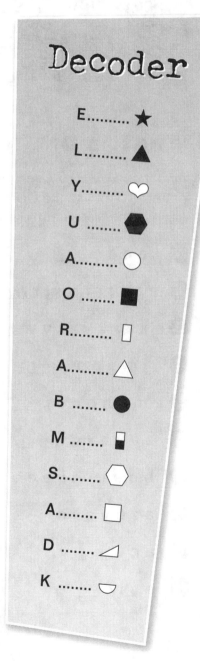

Decoder

E......... ★

L......... ▲

Y......... ♡

U .... ⬡ (filled hexagon)

A......... ○

O .... ■

R......... ▯

A......... △

B .... ●

M .... ◲

S......... ⬡

A......... □

D .... ◹

K .... ◡

1 □□△□□ _____

2 ○△□○△ _____

3 ○△□□△ _____

4 ★△○★△△○★△△△○ _____

5 △◿△◿△△◿△ _____

6 □▯△△□ _____

7 ◡◹◡◡◹◡▯◡◡◡ _____

8 ⬡△△△⬡△△⬡⬡ _____

9 ♡♡♡□♡♡□□ _____

10 ◲◲⊠◲◲◲◲⊠⊠◲◲◲ _____

EACH __ __ __ __ __ __ __ __ __ __.
      10 3 7 4 8   2   9 1 6 5

29

Riddle 26

How much money do a dozen deer have?

What to Do

Find the answer by completing the next step in the pattern. Then use the Decoder to solve the riddle by filling in the blanks at the bottom of the page.

1 a b c c b ___

2 r r s r r r s s r r r ___

3 x x x y y x x y y ___

4 j m p p m j j ___

5 m n n o o o p ___

6 z a y b x c w ___

7 b e e a n t b e e a ___

8 a z b y c x d ___

9 a c e g ___

10 a e i o ___

Decoder

p	V
c	A
w	W
i	U
x	E
o	D
d	B
y	J
h	O
a	E
s	I
u	L
f	G
r	S
m	K
l	Y
k	M
n	C
z	P

T __ __ __ __ __   __ __ __ __ __
  8 3 10 5 1   6 9 7 4 2

Riddle 27

Who is the best fencer in the ocean?

What to Do

Find the answer. Then use the Decoder to solve the riddle by filling in the blanks at the bottom of the page.

1 It is 2 p.m. What time will it be in 2 hours? _____

2 How many hours are between 3 p.m. and 8 p.m.? _____

3 How many hours are between 9 a.m. and 11:30 a.m.? _____

4 It's 10 a.m. What time will it be in 5 hours? _____

5 How many hours are between 8 a.m. and 4 p.m.? _____

6 It's 3 p.m. What time will it be in 45 minutes? _____

7 It's 2:15 p.m., What time will it be in half an hour? _____

8 It's 7:52 p.m. What time was it 25 minutes earlier? _____

9 It's 6:15 p.m. What time will it be in 1 hour and 40 minutes? _____

10 It's 11:07 a.m. What time will it be in 2 hours and 30 minutes? _____

Decoder

2:45 p.m.	S
7:27 a.m.	A
8 hours	F
2:30 p.m.	W
2 1/2 hours	I
1:37 p.m.	R
8:17 p.m.	G
7:55 p.m.	W
3 hours	O
7:27 p.m	H
1:45 p.m.	E
4 p.m	D
1:27 p.m.	K
3:45 p.m.	O
2:15 p.m	T
2 p.m.	Q
5 hours	S
1 1/2 hours	B
3 p.m.	E

TH __ __ __ __ __ __ __ __ __ __
    4   2 9 6 10 1 5 3 7 8

Riddle 28

What part of a cowboy is the saddest?

What to Do

Find the answer. Then use the Decoder to solve the riddle by filling in the blanks at the bottom of the page.

1 Time in New York is one hour later than time in Chicago.
If it's 10 a.m. in New York, what time is it in Chicago? ___

2 If it's 4 p.m. in New York, what time is it in Chicago? ___

3 If it's 8:30 p.m. in Chicago, what time is it in New York? ___

4 Time in New York is three hours later than time in Los Angeles.
If it's 10 a.m. in New York, what time is it in Los Angeles? ___

5 If it's 2:30 p.m. in New York, what time is it in Los Angeles? ___

6 If it's 5:20 a.m. in Los Angeles, what time is it in New York? ___

7 When it is 11:17 a.m. in New York, it is 8:17 a.m.
in Los Angeles. When it's 11:17 a.m. in Los Angeles,
what time is it in New York? ___

8 Time in Los Angeles is two hours earlier
than time in Chicago. If it's 8 p.m. in Los Angeles,
what time is it in Chicago? ___

9 When it's 6 p.m. in Los Angeles, it's 9 p.m. in New York.
What time is it in Chicago? ___

10 When it's 3:11 p.m. in Chicago, it's 4:11 p.m.
in New York. What time is it in Los Angeles? ___

Decoder

8:20 a.m.	**E**
3:00 p.m.	**J**
2:20 a.m.	**K**
5:11 p.m.	**C**
11:30 a.m.	**L**
5:30 p.m.	**I**
8:00 p.m.	**N**
2:17 p.m.	**S**
1:11 p.m	**E**
11:00 a.m.	**M**
12:11 p.m.	**O**
9:00 a.m.	**U**
11:00 p.m.	**T**
6:00 a.m.	**W**
9:30 p.m.	**A**
7:30 p.m.	**Z**
10:00 p.m.	**B**
7:00 a.m.	**S**
2:00 p.m	**G**

HI __ __ __ __ __ __ __ __ __ __
   4   8 5 1 10   2 6 3 9 7

Riddle 29

What do basketball players read in their spare time?

Decoder

6 .... **Q**

9 .... **N**

12 .... **L**

100 .... **B**

36 .... **T**

25 .... **V**

412 .... **O**

730 .... **C**

112 .... **L**

24 .... **E**

15 .... **P**

720 .... **A**

4 .... **S**

20 .... **M**

7 .... **L**

60 .... **A**

3 .... **T**

What to Do

Find the answers. Then use the Decoder to solve the riddle by filling in the blanks at the bottom of the page.

1 How many inches are in 1 foot? _____

2 How many feet are in 1 yard? _____

3 How many days are in 1 week? _____

4 How many hours are in 1 day? _____

5 How many quarts are in 1 gallon? _____

6 How many inches are in 3 feet? _____

7 How many feet are in 20 yards? _____

8 How many days are in 16 weeks? _____

9 How many hours are in 30 days? _____

6   9   1   3   2   7   8   4   5

Riddle 30

What kind of geese come from Portugal?

What to Do

Find the answers. Then use the Decoder to solve the riddle by filling in the blanks at the bottom of the page.

1 How many minutes are in 1 hour? _____

2 How many minutes are in 3 hours? _____

3 How many minutes are in half an hour? _____

4 How many seconds are in 1 minute? _____

5 How many seconds are in 5 minutes? _____

6 How many seconds are in 10 minutes? _____

7 How many minutes are in 1/4 of an hour? _____

8 How many minutes are in 1 hour and 20 minutes? _____

9 How many seconds are in 42 minutes? _____

10 How many seconds are in 13 1/2 minutes? _____

Decoder

60 minutes ...... **E**

2,520 minutes **F**

300 minutes .... **B**

80 minutes ...... **P**

6 minutes .... **A**

2,520 seconds **U**

100 seconds.... **W**

120 minutes .... **N**

180 minutes .... **R**

30 seconds...... **I**

15 minutes ...... **T**

810 seconds.... **E**

200 seconds.... **P**

20 minutes ...... **M**

600 seconds.... **S**

300 seconds.... **O**

60 seconds...... **G**

180 seconds.... **C**

30 minutes ...... **E**

" __ __ __ __ " __ __ __ __ __

  8 5 2 7   9   4 10 3 6 1

Riddle 31

Why do people with colds get plenty of exercise?

What to Do

Find the answers. Then use the Decoder to solve the riddle by filling in the blanks at the bottom of the page.

1 What is the perimeter of this square? _____

2 What is the perimeter of this rectangle? _____

3 What is the perimeter of this triangle? _____

4 What is the perimeter of a square that is 10 inches long on one side? _____

5 A square's perimeter is 48 inches. How long is one side of the square? _____

6 A triangle with three equal sides has a perimeter of 27 inches. How long is one side of the triangle? _____

7 Each side of a pentagon is 11 inches long. What is the pentagon's perimeter? _____

8 What is the perimeter of this shape? _____

9 A magazine is 11 inches long and 8 inches wide. What is the magazine's perimeter? _____

10 A lawn is 23 feet long and 14 feet wide. What is the lawn's perimeter? _____

Decoder

19	O
74 inches......	Q
30	N
25	A
38 inches......	I
12 inches......	S
40 feet	X
9 inches........	N
15	B
74 feet	R
16	E
10 feet	D
20	R
22	A
32 inches......	L
37 feet	M
40 inches......	U
55 inches......	S
15	C

THE __ __   __ __ __ __ __   __ __ __.
9   2   8   3   5   1   7   10   4   6

Riddle 32

What kinds of horses frighten ranchers?

What to Do

Find the answers. Then use the Decoder to solve the riddle by filling in the blanks at the bottom of the page.

1 A triangle has ___ sides.

2 A shape with 4 sides of equal length is called a _____ .

3 A shape with 5 sides is called a _____ .

4 A shape with 8 sides is called a _____ .

5 A hexagon has ___ sides.

6 The distance across a circle is called the _____ .

7 A polygon with 4 sides is called a _____ .

8 A nonagon has ___ sides.

9 All the angles in an equilateral triangle are _____ .

10 Four rectangles have a total of ____ sides

Decoder

9	S
radius............	Y
12	B
square	H
rectangle	F
diameter	R
16	G
equal	E
3	A
heptagon	W
6	I
rhombus	K
8	P
pentagon	N
circumference	D
4	L
quadrilateral ..	T
different	O
5	C
octagon	M

" __ __ __ __ __ " __ __ __ __ __
  3 5 10 2 7   4 1 6 9 8

Riddle 33

What is the last thing that the trapeze flier wants to be?

What to Do

Find the symmetrical shapes. Then use the Decoder to solve the riddle by filling in the blanks at the bottom of the page.

1 _____

2 _____

3 _____

4 _____

5 _____

6 _____

7 _____

8 _____

9 _____

10 _____

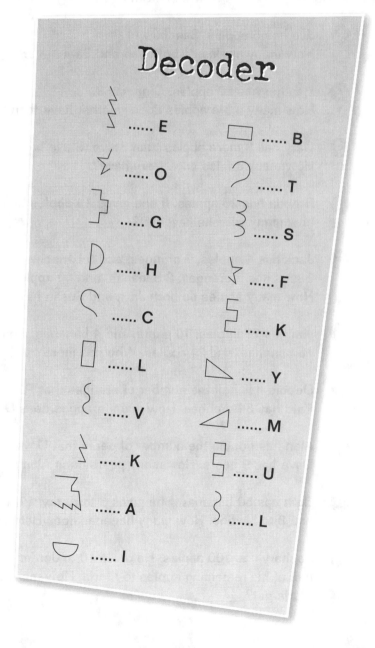

Decoder

..... E   ..... B

..... O   ..... T

..... G   ..... S

..... H   ..... F

..... C   ..... K

..... L   ..... Y

..... V   ..... M

..... K   ..... U

..... A   L

..... I

‾6‾ ‾3‾ ‾9‾   ‾4‾ ‾10‾ ‾1‾ ‾7‾   ‾5‾ ‾8‾ ‾2‾

Riddle 34

What is a ten without its number-one friend?

What to Do

Find the answers. Then use the Decoder to solve the riddle by filling in the blanks at the bottom of the page.

1 Joe has 5 apples. Sam has 11.
How many apples do both Joe and Sam have? _____

2 Heather has 20 apples. Gina has 9.
How many more apples does Heather have than Gina? _____

3 Gary has 8 more apples than Steve. Steve has 32 apples.
How many apples does Gary have? _____

4 Brenda has 25 apples. If she gives 19 apples to Julie,
how many will she have left? _____

5 Jack has 4 apples, 7 oranges, and 9 bananas.
Susan has 8 oranges, 2 bananas, and 10 apples.
How many apples do both Jack and Susan have? _____

6 Jim has 23 apples, 16 pears, and 4 bananas. Holly has 8 pears,
13 bananas, and 21 apples. Who has more fruit? _____

7 Debbie has half the number of oranges that Patti has.
Patti has 34 oranges. How many oranges does Debbie have? ___

8 Alan has double the number of pears that Dave has.
Dave has 9 pears. How many pears does Alan have? _____

9 Beth has 50 bananas. She gives 5 to Kathy, 12 to Jeff,
and 8 to Nadine. How many bananas does Beth have left? _____

10 Zachary has 100 apples. He gives 10 to Jeremy. Then he gives
half of his remaining apples to Maria. How many apples does
Maria get? _____

Decoder

Holly...............	C
24 apples	F
9 apples	U
18 oranges	I
20 oranges	K
16 apples	T
25 apples	M
18 pears	O
50 apples	S
17 oranges	Z
45 apples	A
14 apples	R
6 apples	A
5 apples	R
25 bananas......	T
Jim	O
40 apples	E
32 pears	W
11 apples	L

___ ___ ___ ___ ___ ___ ___ ___ ___ ___
4   1   6   9 10   2   7   3   5   8

What is a mile high and spins?

What to Do

Find the answers. Then use the Decoder to solve the riddle by filling in the blanks at the bottom of the page.

1 Cliff has 4 glasses of water. He drinks 2 of them. Then he drinks 1/2 of the remaining glasses. How many glasses of water does he drink in all? _____

2 Hannah has 8 glasses of lemonade. She drinks 1 glass. Then she drinks 2 glasses. How many glasses of lemonade are left? _____

3 Max has 3 glasses of orange juice and 4 glasses of apple juice. He drinks 1/2 of the glasses of apple juice and 2 glasses of orange juice. How many glasses of juice does he drink? _____

4 Emma is wearing 2 blue socks. Kara is wearing 1 blue sock and 1 black sock. Debbie is wearing 1 black sock and 1 white sock. How many black socks are being worn? _____

5 Jane owns 6 pairs of boots. How many boots does Jane own? _____

6 Alex owns 50 pairs of sneakers. Twenty pairs are for running. Sixteen pairs are for basketball. Fourteen pairs are for tennis. How many pairs of sneakers are not basketball sneakers? _____

7 Carol owns 3 dogs. What is the total number of pairs of dog legs? ____

8 Carol walks with her 3 dogs in the park. What is the total number of legs walking in the park? _____

9 A person has 2 legs. That is 1/4 of the number of legs a spider has. How many legs does a spider have? _____

10 Who has more legs: 2 spiders, 7 people, or 3 dogs? _____

Decoder

3 glasses	**U**
7 people......	**E**
8 legs.........	**P**
4 legs.........	**C**
10 boots	**X**
14 legs........	**O**
5 glasses	**T**
2 black socks	**I**
24 pairs	**L**
12 boots	**N**
6 glasses	**R**
34 pairs	**N**
4 black socks	**D**
2 spiders	**A**
6 boots	**S**
6 pairs	**O**
3 dogs	**H**
4 glasses	**T**

A M __ __ __ __ __ __ __ __ __ __
    7 1 5 3 10 4 6   2 8 9

Riddle 36

What did the bored cow say when she got up in the morning?

What to Do

Find the answers. Then use the Decoder to solve the riddle by filling in the blanks at the bottom of the page.

Decoder

6 years	F
21	Y
60	O
26	E
36	U
31	I
8 years	S
9	A
13	M
4 years	A
74	N
15 years	R
20	D
5 years	R
17	P
7	D
18	H
11 years	D

1 Hank was born in 1990. How old was he in 1997? _____

2 How much older was Hank in 1996 than he was in 1992? ____

3 Amy was born in 1985. How old was she in 1994? _____

4 Leon was born in 1979. How old will he be in the year 2000? _____

5 Lisa is 20 years older than Abby. When Lisa is 40, how old will Abby be? _____

6 In 1995, Howard was 11 years old and Beverly was 19 years old. In the year 2012, how old will Beverly be? _____

7 Mary is 4 years older than Jerry. Jerry is 7 years older than Bill. How much older is Mary than Bill? _____

8 George is half as old as Ellen. George is 37 years old. How old is Ellen? _____

9 Tony is 15 years older than Tim. Ned is 10 years younger than Tony. How much older is Ned than Tim? ____

10 When Elizabeth is 3 years old, Joan is 16 years old. How old will Joan be when Elizabeth is exactly half her age? _____

"**JUST** __ __ __ __ __ __ __ __ __."
　　　　　2　8　　6　7　1　10　9　　5　3　4

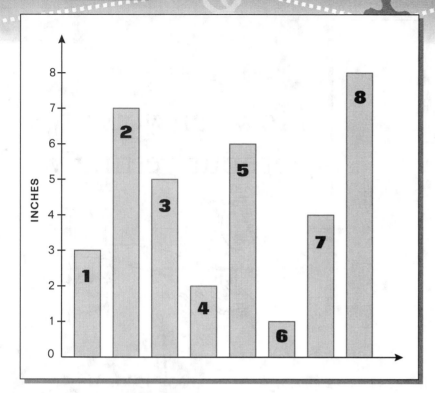

Riddle 37

Why did the horse sneeze?

KACHOO!

What to Do

Answer each question about the graph. Then use the Decoder to solve the riddle by filling in the blanks at the bottom of the page.

1 Which is the tallest bar on the graph? _____

2 Which is the shortest bar on the graph? _____

3 How tall is bar 1? _____

4 How much taller is bar 5 than bar 4? _____

5 How much shorter is bar 4 than bar 2? _____

6 How tall is bar 8? _____

7 Which bar is taller: bar 1 or bar 7? _____

8 Which bar is shorter: bar 2 or bar 3? _____

9 Which bar is twice the size of bar 1? _____

10 How many of bar 4 would equal bar 8? _____

Decoder

4 bars .... **T**
6 inches .... **K**
bar 5 .... **L**
bar 2 .... **A**
bar 6 .... **L**
2 inches .... **U**
2 bars .... **P**
5 inches .... **L**
bar 8 .... **T**
7 inches .... **W**
bar 3 .... **O**
bar 1 .... **S**
3 inches .... **E**
8 inches .... **C**
8 bars .... **M**
4 inches .... **T**
3 bars .... **H**
bar 4 .... **N**
bar 7 .... **I**

IT HAD A __ __ __ __ __ __   "__ __ __ __."

2   7   10   4   9   3   6   8   5   1

41

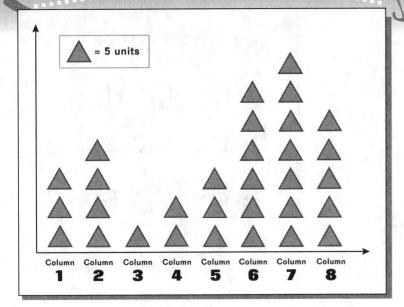

= 5 units

Column 1 Column 2 Column 3 Column 4 Column 5 Column 6 Column 7 Column 8

Riddle 38

How can you dive without getting wet?

What to Do

Answer the questions about the graph. Then use the Decoder to solve the riddle by filling in the blanks at the bottom of the page.

1 How many units does one ▲ equal? _____

2 Which column has the most units? _____

3 Which column has the fewest units? _____

4 How many units are in column 2? _____

5 Which columns have the same number of units? _____

6 How many units are in column 8? _____

7 How many more units are in column 6 than in column 5? _____

8 How many fewer units are in column 3 than in column 7? _____

9 If the number of ▲s doubled in column 2, how many units would be in the column? _____

10 Which column has 1/3 of the units of column 6? _____

Decoder

40 units .... **G**
50 units .... **A**
column 7 ...... **S**
column 1 ...... **P**
column 4 ...... **K**
30 units .... **N**
columns 2 and 8 .... **E**
25 units .... **O**
20 units .... **I**
column 6 ...... **H**
35 units .... **W**
5 units .... **D**
15 units .... **V**
column 8 ...... **T**
10 units .... **L**
column 3 ...... **I**
columns 1 and 5 .... **Y**

G __ __ __ __ __ __ __ __ __ __.
  6   2 10 5 1 4 7 3 8 9

What do cheerleaders like to drink?

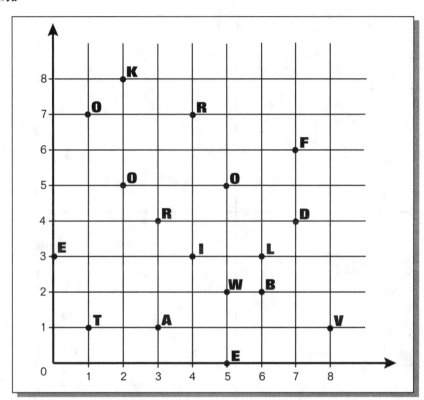

What to Do

Use the coordinates to identify points on the graph. Then use the point names to solve the riddle by filling in the blanks at the bottom of the page.

1 (1,1) _____   **6** (2,5) _____

2 (3,4) _____   **7** (0,3) _____

3 (4,7) _____   **8** (1,7) _____

4 (6,2) _____   **9** (7,6) _____

5 (5,5) _____   **10** (5,0) _____

LOTS __ __   __ __ __ __   __ __ __ __
        5 9   2 6 8 1   4 7 10 3

43

Riddle 40

What do baby sweet potatoes sleep in?

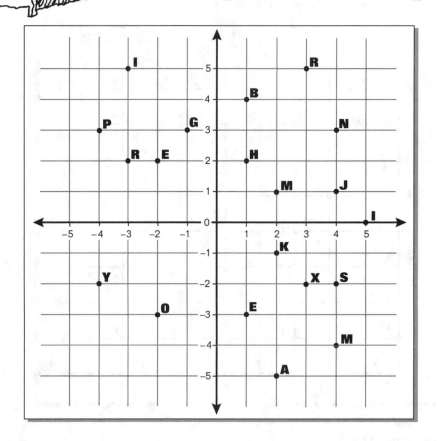

What to Do

Use the coordinates to identify points on the graph. Then use the point names to solve the riddle by filling in the blanks at the bottom of the page.

1 (2,1) _____   **6** (2,-5) _____

2 (3,5) _____   **7** (-2,2) _____

3 (4,-2) _____   **8** (-3,5) _____

4 (5,0) _____   **9** (4,-4) _____

5 (1,-3) _____   **10** (-4,-2) _____

TH __ __ __   " __ __ __ __ __ __ "
     7   4   2   10   6   9   1   8   5   3

Answers

Riddle 1 (Place Value)

1.	9	6.	108
2.	22	7.	86
3.	17	8.	153
4.	45	9.	370
5.	67	10.	534

Where do cows go for entertainment?

To the "moo"vies

Riddle 2 (Place Value)

1.	912
2.	1,071
3.	4,804
4.	7,130
5.	13,650
6.	40,002
7.	70,875
8.	500,000
9.	260,927
10.	1,817,104

What did the helmet say to the football player?

"You're putting me on."

Riddle 3 (Place Value)

1.	tens place	6.	32
2.	3	7.	174
3.	ones place	8.	799
4.	0	9.	2,012
5.	2	10.	7

What happens when skiers get old?

They go downhill.

Riddle 4 (Place Value)

1.	thousands
2.	6
3.	tens
4.	7
5.	0
6.	billions
7.	hundred millions
8.	727,912
9.	4,847,266
10.	7,446,732,011

How do skunks measure length?

In "scent"imeters

Riddle 5 (Addition)

1.	19	6.	165
2.	42	7.	245
3.	54	8.	368
4.	35	9.	768
5.	66	10.	1,323

What sickness can't you talk about until it's cured?

Laryngitis

Riddle 6 (Addition)

1.	1,804
2.	689
3.	1,063
4.	2,133
5.	3,489
6.	8,234
7.	7,538
8.	8,292
9.	5,429
10.	10,439

What's the best thing to eat in a bathtub?

Sponge cake

Riddle 7 (Subtraction)

1.	6	6.	37
2.	3	7.	97
3.	28	8.	11
4.	8	9.	64
5.	18	10.	486

When is the ocean friendliest?

When it waves.

Riddle 8 (Subtraction)

1.	257	6.	2,869
2.	428	7.	459
3.	300	8.	48
4.	743	9.	4,884
5.	1,451	10.	7,926

What tables grow on farms?

"Vege"tables

Riddle 9 (Rounding)

1.	10
2.	20
3.	50
4.	90
5.	200
6.	400
7.	600
8.	300
9.	500
10.	700

What did the farmer get when he tried to reach the beehive?

A "buzzy" signal

Riddle 10 (Rounding)

1.	800
2.	5,000
3.	3,700
4.	1,000
5.	2,770
6.	8,000
7.	24,400
8.	11,000
9.	9,940
10.	73,000

What do cows give after an earthquake?

Milk shakes

Riddle 11 (Multiplication)

1.	30
2.	70
3.	81
4.	68
5.	125
6.	400
7.	660
8.	720
9.	342
10.	3,312

What is a tree's favorite drink?

A cold root beer

Riddle 12 (Multiplication)

1. 4,000
2. 3,604
3. 20,564
4. 45,288
5. 304,512
6. 100,000
7. 1,060,000
8. 2,384,394
9. 924,000
10. 170,017

What's the one thing you can always count on?

Your fingers

Riddle 13 (Multiplication)

1. 142,758
2. 429,598
3. 288,400
4. 404,928
5. 4,953,740
6. 2,634,352
7. 5,220,972
8. 49,220,633
9. 32,634,196
10. 100,541,060

Which month has 28 days?

All of them do.

Riddle 14 (Division)

1. 4
2. 2
3. 6
4. 5
5. 8
6. 3 remainder 2
7. 6 remainder 6
8. 9 remainder 2
9. 8 remainder 1
10. 15 remainder 2

What kind of tools do you use for math?

"Multi"pliers

Riddle 15 (Division)

1. 14 remainder 4
2. 2 remainder 8
3. 10 remainder 1
4. 5 remainder 5
5. 2 remainder 9
6. 3
7. 4 remainder 16
8. 9 remainder 1
9. 4
10. 8

What has 18 legs and catches flies?

A baseball team

Riddle 16 (Division)

1. 4
2. 20 remainder 10
3. 11
4. 6 remainder 58
5. 9 remainder 7
6. 9 remainder 50
7. 5
8. 33 remainder 12
9. 30 remainder 40
10. 30 remainder 23

What has 3 feet but can't run?

A yardstick

Riddle 17 (Fraction Identification)

1. 1/2
2. 3/4
3. 2/7
4. 3/5
5. 5/9
6. 7/11
7. 5/8
8. 3/8
9. 3/10
10. 1/9

What do joggers say when they leave you?

"So long, got to run."

Riddle 18 (Fraction Addition)

1. 1
2. 2/4
3. 4/5
4. 5/7
5. 7/9
6. 12/13
7. 19/25
8. 29/40
9. 86/102
10. 193/237

How does a farmer count his cows?

With a "cow"culator

Riddle 19 (Fraction Subtraction)

1. 1/3
2. 3/8
3. 3/11
4. 14/20
5. 1/32
6. 20/67
7. 59/83
8. 22/121
9. 3/156
10. 99/312

What did one magnet say to the other magnet?

"You attract me**."**

Riddle 20 (Fraction Multiplication)

1. 1
2. 4/5
3. 4
4. 5
5. 6/7
6. 16/6
7. 56/17
8. 6/12
9. 2/35
10. 108/187

What eight-letter word only contains one letter?

An envelope

Riddle 21 (Money)

1. $5.00
2. $16.00
3. $2.00
4. $9.00
5. $4.50
6. $10.37
7. 70 cents
8. 75 cents
9. 45 cents
10. $2.85

Why didn't the eagle get its hair wet when it went swimming?

It was a bald eagle.

Riddle 22 (Money)

1. $3.00
2. $35.00
3. 55 cents
4. $1.00
5. $52.00
6. $57.50
7. $9.00
8. $3.25
9. $138.00
10. $322.00

How is medicine packed for astronauts?

In space capsules

Riddle 23 (Number Patterns)

1. 10
2. 9
3. 19
4. 25
5. 160
6. 7
7. 35
8. 15
9. 144
10. 400

What would you get if a pig learned karate?

Some pork chops

Riddle 24 (Number Patterns)

1. 1
2. 4
3. 22
4. 26
5. 34
6. 57
7. 115
8. 124
9. 60
10. 215

How can you make the number seven even?

Take away the "s."

Riddle 25 (Shape Patterns)

1. △
2. □
3. ○
4. ★
5. ◿
6. ▯
7. ▽
8. ⬡
9. ♡
10. ◨

What do 36 inches and grass have in common?

Each makes a yard.

Riddle 26 (Letter Patterns)

1. a
2. r
3. x
4. m
5. p
6. d
7. n
8. w
9. i
10. u

How much money do a dozen deer have?

Twelve bucks

Riddle 27 (Time)

1. 4 p.m.
2. 5 hours
3. 2 1/2 hours
4. 3 p.m.
5. 8 hours
6. 3:45 p.m.
7. 2:45 p.m.
8. 7:27 p.m.
9. 7:55 p.m.
10. 1:37 p.m.

Who is the best fencer in the ocean?

The swordfish

Riddle 28 (Time)

1. 9 a.m.
2. 3 p.m.
3. 9:30 p.m.
4. 7 a.m.
5. 11:30 a.m.
6. 8:20 a.m.
7. 2:17 p.m.
8. 10 p.m.
9. 8 p.m.
10. 1:11 p.m.

What part of a cowboy is the saddest?

His blue jeans

Riddle 29 (Measurement)

1. 12
2. 3
3. 7
4. 24
5. 4
6. 36
7. 60
8. 112
9. 720

What do basketball players read in their spare time?

Tall tales

Riddle 30 (Measurement and Time)

1. 60 minutes
2. 180 minutes
3. 30 minutes
4. 60 seconds
5. 300 seconds
6. 600 seconds
7. 15 minutes
8. 80 minutes
9. 2,520 seconds
10. 810 seconds

What kind of geese come from Portugal?

"Portu"geese

Riddle 31 (Perimeter)

1. 16
2. 20
3. 19
4. 40 inches
5. 12 inches
6. 9 inches
7. 55 inches
8. 30
9. 38 inches
10. 74 feet

Why do people with colds get plenty of exercise?

Their noses run.

Riddle 32 (Geometry)

1. 3
2. square
3. pentagon
4. octagon
5. 6
6. diameter
7. quadrilateral
8. 9
9. equal
10. 16

What kinds of horses frighten ranchers?

"Night"mares

Riddle 33 (Symmetry)

1. □   6. ⌒
2. ◁   7. ⌇
3. ◗   8. ⌇
4. ⌄   9. ⌇
5. ⌐   10. ⌇

What is the last thing that the trapeze flier wants to be?

The fall guy

Riddle 34 (Word Problems)

1. 16 apples
2. 11 apples
3. 40 apples
4. 6 apples
5. 14 apples
6. Jim
7. 17 oranges
8. 18 pears
9. 25 bananas
10. 45 apples

What is a ten without its number-one friend?

A total zero

Riddle 35 (Word Problems)

1. 3 glasses
2. 5 glasses
3. 4 glasses
4. 2 black socks
5. 12 boots
6. 34 pairs
7. 6 pairs
8. 14 legs
9. 8 legs
10. 2 spiders

What is a mile high and spins?

A mountain top

Riddle 36 (Word Problems)

1. 7
2. 4 years
3. 9
4. 21
5. 20
6. 36
7. 11 years
8. 74
9. 5 years
10. 26

What did the bored cow say when she got up in the morning?

"Just an udder day."

Riddle 37 (Bar Graph)

1. bar 8
2. bar 6
3. 3 inches
4. 4 inches
5. 5 inches
6. 8 inches
7. bar 7
8. bar 3
9. bar 5
10. 4

Why did the horse sneeze?

It had a little "colt."

Riddle 38 (Pictograph)

1. 5 units
2. column 7
3. column 3
4. 20 units
5. columns 1 and 5
6. 25 units
7. 15 units
8. 30 units
9. 40 units
10. column 4

How can you dive without getting wet?

Go skydiving.

Riddle 39 (Coordinate Graphing)

1. T   6. O
2. R   7. E
3. R   8. O
4. B   9. F
5. O   10. E

What do cheerleaders like to drink?

Lots of root beer

Riddle 40 (Coordinate Graphing)

1. M   6. A
2. R   7. E
3. S   8. I
4. I   9. M
5. E   10. Y

What do baby sweet potatoes sleep in?

Their "yammies"